B1 Topic 1 — Variatio

B1 Topic 1 — Variation

Page 1 — Classification

Q1 a) Prokaryotes
b) E.g. they don't have chlorophyll / they're saprophytes not autotrophs.
c) E.g. they're unicellular.
d) Because they're non-living.
Q3 a) class, order, family, genus
b) i) E.g. they contain chlorophyll, they're autotrophs.
ii) E.g. they're multicellular, they're heterotrophs.
c) They all have a supporting rod-like structure that goes up the back of the body.
Q3 a) Vertebrates have a backbone and an internal skeleton but invertebrates don't.
b) How they absorb oxygen, how they reproduce, how they regulate their internal body temperature.
c) Some species don't really fit into any of the categories — they have features of more than one category. (E.g. the duck-billed platypus is classed as a mammal because it has similar features to other mammals, but it lays eggs too.)

Page 2 — More on Classification

Q1 It looks like a fern. (It does not produce seeds, but does have long stems with lots of small leaves.)
Q2 a) Western greenish warbler and Two-barred warbler
b) ring species
Q3 a) Binomial means a two-part name (one name for the genus and one for the species).
b) Any three from: it helps scientists to identify different species / it helps scientists to study species / it helps scientists to conserve species / it helps scientists to target conservation efforts.
Q4 a) Because it contradicts the species definition — the plants don't interbreed but they still might be the same species.
b) Because it contradicts the species definition — according to it, all these ducks should be the same species. However, they're not the same species because they're really different in many other ways, e.g. in genetics.

Pages 3-4 — Variation

Q1 have differences, genes, Identical twins, hair style, environment, variation
Q2 a) genes
b) genes
c) genes
d) environment
e) genes (also accept 'both', as the colour of a plant's flowers can sometimes be affected by environment, e.g. mineral content of the soil).
f) both
Q3 a) No. Identical twins have exactly the same genes. Features like hair colour are controlled by genes, so you would expect the girls to have the same hair colour.
b) The difference in weight must be due to environment (e.g. eating more or exercising less), because the twins have exactly the same genes.
c) I don't think that birthmarks are caused by genes. Identical twins have exactly the same genes, so if Stephanie had a birthmark then Helen should too if it was genetic.
Q4 a) Sexual reproduction gives new combinations of genes, so the foal might not be genetically suited to racing. / Organisms are affected by their environment as well as their genes.
b) genes

Q5 a) To make hi ... ... the average hei, ...uce the effect of any extreme results.
b) i) To make it a fair test — only the concentration of minerals should be affecting the plants.
ii) E.g. any two of: amount of water / light intensity / temperature.
c) The higher the mineral concentration (up to 500 ppm), the faster their growth.
d) The plants were affected by both their genes and their environment. The height of the plants is affected by their genes as the different species are different heights — they have different genetic material. The plants are also strongly affected by their environment — their height increases with the mineral concentration.

Page 5 — Continuous and Discontinuous Variation

Q1 a) discontinuous
b) continuous
c) discontinuous
d) continuous
e) discontinuous
Q2 E.g. measure and record the hand span of everyone in the class to get a range of data. Draw a graph to show the data.
Q3 a) i) Discontinuous variation is when there are two or more distinct categories — each individual falls into only one of these categories, there are no intermediates.
ii) seed colour
b) i) Continuous variation is when the individuals in a population vary within a range — there are no distinct categories.
ii) length of pea pods
c) graph A

Pages 6-7 — Extreme Environments

Q1 a) There is no light so plants can't grow and food is scarce. There are very high pressures so deep under the water. It is often very cold at such a depth.
b) The light attracts prey.
c) E.g. it is able to scoop up food from the sea bed / eat large fish.
Q2 a) Heat and minerals / chemicals.
b) i) Chemosynthesis.
ii) The process involves using chemical energy to make food.
c) bacteria
Q3 a) The kangaroo rat.
b) The polar bear.
c) The polar bear has a rounded body shape, which means it has a small surface area for its volume.
d) Less heat.
e) Its thick layer of blubber provides insulation. Its big feet spread its weight to stop it sinking into snow or breaking ice. Its greasy fur sheds water, preventing cooling due to evaporation.
Q4 a) The muscles moving the feet and flippers will stay warmer and so will be able to work better.
b) It helps them to conserve heat.

Pages 8-9 — Natural Selection and Evidence for Evolution

Q1 It's the slow and continuous change of organisms from one generation to the next.
Q2 common, more recently, gradual, more, similar

B1 Topic 1 — Variation

Q3 The best adapted animals and plants are most likely to survive.
Some characteristics are passed on through reproduction from parent to offspring.
Individuals less well adapted to their environment are less likely to survive and reproduce.

Q4 The poison warfarin was used to kill rats. But a certain gene gives rats resistance to warfarin — these rats are more likely to survive and breed. So now there are rat populations that are warfarin-resistant.

Q5 Any two from: Scientists publish their work in scientific journals. If other scientists can repeat the same experiments and get the same results, the scientific community can be pretty confident that the evidence is reliable. / Before scientists can publish their work it has to undergo peer review. Other scientists read and review the work, to check it's valid and that experiments are carried out to the highest possible standards. / Scientists attend scientific conferences to present and discuss their work. They're an easy way for the latest theories and evidence to be shared and discussed.

Q6 a) The lighter moth was better camouflaged against the bark of the trees, so it was less likely to be spotted and eaten by birds.
b) As industry increased, the trees became darkened with soot. Now the dark moths were better camouflaged to escape predation by birds, so they increased in number.
c) Genes.

Page 10 — Speciation and Genes

Q1 nucleus, chromosomes, DNA, genes
Q2 gene, chromosome, nucleus, cell
Q3 a) 'Alleles' are different forms of the same gene.
b) Alleles give different versions of a characteristic.
Q4 a) Isolation is where populations of a species are separated.
b) 1 — There are two populations of the same species.
2 — Physical barriers separate the populations.
3 — The populations adapt to their new environments.
4 — A new species develops.

Pages 11-12 — Genetic Diagrams

Q1 dominant — shown in organisms heterozygous for that trait
genotype — the alleles that an individual contains
heterozygous — having two different alleles for a gene
homozygous — having two identical alleles for a gene
phenotype — the actual characteristics of an individual
recessive — not shown in organisms heterozygous for that trait
Q2 a) Wilma will have brown hair.
b) Wilma has two different alleles for this gene so she is heterozygous for the characteristic.
Q3 a) i) red eyes
ii) white eyes
iii) red eyes
iv) white eyes
b) i)

		parent's alleles	
		R	r
parent's alleles	R	RR	Rr
	r	Rr	rr

ii) 1/4 or 25%
iii) 12

Q4 a)

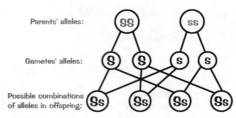

b) 0% chance of being wrinkled.
c)

		parent's alleles	
		S	s
parent's alleles	S	SS	Ss
	s	Ss	ss

d) true

Pages 13-14 — Genetic Diagrams and Disorders

Q1 a) Any two of, e.g. tiredness / painful joints and muscles / fever / anaemia.
b) i) Aa
ii) aa
iii) AA
Q2 a) genetic, parents, recessive, allele, mucus, pancreas, breathing, lung, carrier
b)

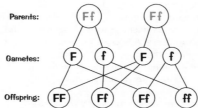

c) i) 3:1
ii) Any one from: 50% / 0.5 / 1 in 2 chance / ½.
Q3 a) Because plenty of the family carry the allele but aren't sufferers.
b) i)

	Carrier	Sufferer
Libby	50%	25%
Anne	50%	0%

ii) Libby
Q4 a) Emma
b) Martha
c) Any one from: 25% / 0.25 / 1 in 4 chance / ¼.
This is because both James and Martha must be carriers to have had children (Mike and Julian) with the disease.

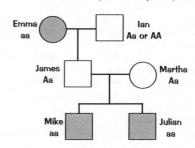

B1 Topic 2 — Responding to Change

Pages 15-16 — Mixed Questions — B1 Topic 1

Q1 a) The second Latin name, which gives the species, is different for the two geese.

b) They belong to the same genus. / The first Latin name is the same.

c) the binomial system

d) Organisms that can interbreed to produce fertile offspring.

e) i) animal kingdom

ii) E.g. they're heterotrophs / multicellular.

Q2 a) Thick fur traps insulating air, which helps to reduce heat loss. White fur provides camouflage.

b) Individuals that are better adapted to their environment are likely to survive longer and reproduce more, so the alleles producing the adaptations become widespread in the population.

c) E.g. the population of Arctic foxes might decrease because there is more competition for resources between the Arctic fox and new species of fox.

Q3 a) E.g. they have differently-shaped shells.

b) genes

c) Because individuals can look really different but still be the same species.

d) i) Yes. Because weight is affected by how much food an animal gets.

ii) Continuous variation. Tortoises can be any weight within a range — there are no distinct categories.

Q4 a) A different version of the same gene.

b)

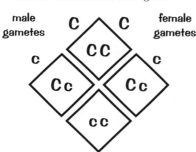

c) Any one from: 25% / 0.25 / 1 in 4 chance / ¼.

B1 Topic 2 — Responding to Change

Page 17 — Homeostasis

Q1 a) The maintenance of a 'stable internal environment' in the body.

b) Any two from: e.g. body temperature / water content / blood glucose level

Q2 nerve, cold, erector, hairs, air

Q3 2 — His brain detects the increase in body temperature.
3 — It triggers a series of responses that make Tim's body temperature fall.
4 — Tim's body temperature drops to a normal level.

Q4 a) hypothalamus

b) The water in sweat evaporates and transfers heat to the environment, cooling you down.

c) i) Vasodilation is the expansion of blood vessels. Vasoconstriction is the constriction of the blood vessels.

ii) Vasodilation and vasoconstriction allow the body to control the blood flow near the surface of the skin. This allows the body to lose or retain heat in response to the environmental temperature.

Page 18 — Hormones and Nerves

Q1 chemicals, endocrine, blood, target, slow, long

Q2 Any two from: e.g. hormones produce a slower response than nerves / Hormones act for a longer time than nerves. / Hormones act in a more general way than nerves. / Hormones are chemical messages, nerve signals are electrical.

Q3 Only the cells with the correct receptor molecules on their surfaces will respond, and only the target cells have these receptors.

Q4 a)

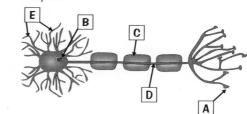

b) i) They connect the neurone with lots of other neurones.

ii) It acts as an electrical insulator, which stops the impulse getting lost. It also speeds up the electrical impulse.

c) They diffuse across the synapse and set off a new electrical impulse in the next neurone.

Pages 19-20 — The Nervous System

Q1 a) True

b) True

c) True

d) False

Q2 central, brain, spinal, electrical, sensory, motor, effectors

Q3 a) long, short

b) short, short, sensory, motor

c) one long axon

Q4

Sense organ	Receptor type
Eye	Light
Nose	**Smell**
Ear	Sound / balance
Tongue	**Taste**
Skin	Touch / temperature

Q5 Any two from e.g.: so that the animal's internal environment can be changed to fit the external environment. / To detect predators. / To be able to detect food and water. / To detect and present to a mate.

Q6 For the man to register the touch, information from the pressure receptors in his toe needs to be sent to the brain via the spinal cord. If the spinal cord is damaged the information may not reach the brain.

Q7 a)

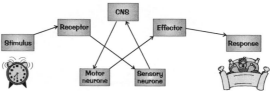

b) i) detect stimuli

ii) carry impulses from receptor cells to the CNS

iii) coordinates responses

iv) carry impulses from the CNS to effector cells

v) carry out a response

c) A change in the environment which you may need to react to.

B1 Topic 2 — Responding to Change

Pages 21-22 — Investigating Stimuli and Reflexes

Q1 a) quickly
b) spinal cord
c) protect
d) without
Q2 a) sensory neurone
b) relay neurone
c) motor neurone
Q3 A reflex reaction can happen more quickly than a voluntary reaction because it doesn't require conscious thought. Often only a few neurones are involved, so the impulse doesn't have to travel as far and can arrive at the effector almost at once.
Q4 A reflex arc is the path taken by nerve impulses to produce a reflex response to a stimulus. It usually consists of a receptor, a sensory neurone, a relay neurone (in the CNS), a motor neurone and an effector.
Q5 a) A sensory neurone.
b) i) Object coming towards your head.
ii) Light receptors in the eye.
iii) The muscles.
iv) Moving your head out of the way.
Q6 a) i) fingertip
ii) sole of foot
b) The fingertip. This was the most sensitive part of the body to pressure, so it must contain the greatest concentration of receptors.
c) John and Marc might have been applying different pressures, so any differences the pupils noticed might not have been due only to the number of receptors.
d) E.g. test each pupil a number of times and find the average.

Pages 23-24 — Insulin and Diabetes

Q1 a) from digested food and drink
b) liver and pancreas
c) insulin and glucagon
Q2 Missing words are: insulin, pancreas, insulin, liver, glycogen, glucose, blood, reduced/lower, insulin.
Q3 Glucagon is secreted by the pancreas. This makes the liver turn glycogen into glucose. Glucose is added by the liver into the blood. So the blood glucose level increases and glucagon stops being secreted.
Q4 a) A condition where the pancreas produces little or no insulin.
b) i) subcutaneous fat
ii) Taking regular exercise reduces the amount of insulin that needs to be injected.
c) A condition where the pancreas doesn't produce enough insulin, or when a person becomes resistant to insulin (their body's cells don't respond properly to the hormone).
d) Any two from: eating a healthy diet / getting regular exercise / losing weight.
e) Obese people have an increased risk of developing type 2 diabetes.
Q5 a) i) 29.2 (to 1 decimal place)
ii) 31.0 (to 1 decimal place)
b) Jim, because he has a BMI of over 30.

Page 25 — Plant Growth Hormones

Q1 a) False
b) True
c) True
d) True
Q2 Lights B and E are broken.
Q3 Positive phototropism — growing towards light.
Positive gravitropism — growing downwards.
Q4 shade, faster, towards, lower, faster, downwards

Q5 a) In shoots, auxin makes the cells grow faster. In the roots, auxin slows cell growth.
b) It increases the area that the roots cover, so enables roots to absorb water and minerals over a greater area of soil.

Page 26 — Plant Growth Hormones — Experiments

Q1 a) Auxin and gibberellin both increase the height of the plants more than just adding water. When auxin and gibberellin are added together they increase the height even more.
b) E.g. repeat the experiment by using several plants for each treatment and the control. Then take the average height for each.
Q2 a) Seedling A: the foil prevents any light reaching the tip, so the auxin is evenly distributed in the tip and no bending occurs.
Seedling C: the mica strip prevents the auxin from moving to the side that's in the shade, so there is even distribution of auxin and no bending occurs.
b) E.g. Vicky could repeat the experiment to improve the reliability of the results.

Page 27 — Commercial Use of Plant Hormones

Q1 E.g. as selective weedkillers / growing cuttings with rooting powder / controlling the ripening of fruit / producing seedless fruit.
Q2 a) E.g. unripe fruit is firmer, so it's less easily damaged during picking and transport.
b) i) E.g. they can be sprayed with a ripening hormone.
ii) During transport to the market.
Q3 a) It increased crop yield compared to the field without the weedkiller.
b) Plant growth hormones disrupt the normal growth patterns of broad-leaved plants (the weeds) but not crops. (This kills the weeds and allows the crops to grow bigger as there is less competition for nutrients and light.)

Pages 28-29 — Mixed Questions — B1 Topic 2

Q1 a) Reflex actions can be faster than normal responses, so can prevent the body being harmed.
b) The central nervous system.
c)

	A	B
stimulus	pressure of the pin	chemicals in the food
receptor	pressure receptors and pain receptors	chemical/smell receptors
effector	muscles in the leg	salivary glands
response	foot is lifted up	saliva released into mouth

Q2 a) Hormones are released into the blood and carried all over the body. They only affect cells that have the right receptors for that particular hormone, but these may be found in several different parts of the body.
b) long-lasting
c) i) synapse
ii) neurotransmitter
d) reflex arc
Q3 a) pancreas
b) i) insulin
ii) E.g. by injecting insulin.
Q4 a) Growth hormone increased height in the poppies but not in the wheat.
b) E.g. as a selective weedkiller.
c) E.g. auxin/gibberellin

B1 Topic 3 — Inter-relationships

B1 Topic 3 — Inter-relationships

Pages 30-31 — Drugs

Q1 a) A chemical substance that affects the central nervous system, which can cause changes in psychological behaviour and can be addictive.

b) Physical addiction means that the body has a physical need for the drug, the person will suffer withdrawal symptoms if no drug is given.

c) The body gets used to the drug and higher doses are needed to produce any / the same effect.

Q2 a)

Type of drug	Example	Effects
Depressants	E.g. alcohol	Decrease brain activity
Painkillers	Morphine	Decrease the feeling of pain
Stimulants	E.g. nicotine / caffeine	Increase the activity of the brain
Hallucinogens	E.g. LSD	Distort what is seen and heard

b) It blocks the nerve impulses in the brain.

Q3 a) Depressants decrease the activity of the brain and nervous system, causing slow reactions and poor judgement.

b) Caffeine is a stimulant which increases the activity of the brain and makes you more alert. It wouldn't negatively affect your reaction times or judgement.

Q4 a) E.g. any two of: Jane might have improved by the third time because of practice. / Jane's finger and thumb might have been different distances from the ruler at the start. / Jane might have been concentrating more at some times and not so much at others. / Sometimes Tom may have made a movement that accidentally gave a clue about when he was going to drop the ruler. / Reaction times might not always be the same, even in the same person. / They may have made a mistake reading off the results.

b) The more variable the readings are, the more repeats you should do. This will help to reduce the effect of any anomalous results and make the final average more reliable.

c) E.g. in case knowing what type of coffee they were given influenced the way they behaved.

d) i)

	Distance before coffee (cm)		Distance after coffee (cm)	
Trial	Tom	Jane	Tom	Jane
Mean	18	15.8	17.5	13.1

ii) Jane

Pages 32-33 — Smoking, Alcohol and Organ Transplants

Q1 a) E.g. lowers inhibitions.

b) Blurs vision.

c) Reactions are slowed down.

Q2 long-term, poisonous, liver, harmless, death, blood, cirrhosis, cleaning, damage, brain

Q3 a) Tobacco smoke contains nicotine, which is addictive.

b) Women who smoke often give birth to underweight babies.

c) Tobacco smoke contains carbon monoxide, which combines with haemoglobin in red blood cells. This means that the blood cells can't carry as much oxygen, depriving the growing baby of oxygen.

Q4 a) Join the NHS organ donor register.

b) family members

c) i) They will benefit from having a healthy liver (dangerous substances can now be removed from the blood, stopping the rest of the body from being damaged).

ii) E.g. some people think they might not deserve it as they have damaged their own liver / they might damage their new liver by continuing to drink.

d) E.g. they might have to lose weight.

Q5 a) 70%

b) The number of smokers in the male population has been decreasing since 1950. The number of female smokers rose between 1950 and 1970, but then it also began to decrease. The number of male smokers has been consistently greater than the number of female smokers.

c) Tobacco smoke contains carcinogens, which are chemicals known to cause cancer.

Pages 34-35 — Infectious Diseases

Q1 a) True
b) False
c) False
d) False

Q2 virus, droplets in air, colds, stay at home, virus, AIDS, body fluids

Q3

Disease	Cholera	Salmonella	Malaria	Athlete's foot
Type of organism	bacterium	bacterium	protozoan	fungus
How it is transmitted	by contaminated water	by contaminated food	by the Anopheles mosquito	by touching contaminated surfaces

Q4 a) E.g. house fly

b) It carries the bacteria that cause dysentery onto food.

Q5 a) Accept answers from 40.5 – 40.75°C.

b) After about 2 days.

Q6 a) Blood clots are used to quickly seal the skin if it's damaged and keep microorganisms out.

b) The air passages are lined with mucus and cilia to trap and remove the bacteria before they reach the lungs.

Q7 1. The eyes produce lysozyme in tears, which kills bacteria on the surface of the eye.
2. The stomach produces hydrochloric acid, which kills pathogens in food.

Q8 a) i) about 5900 cases
ii) in 2000

b) There was a general increase in the number of TB cases between 1997 and 2005.

Page 36 — More About Drugs

Q1 drugs, inside, growing, antibacterials, fungal, cannot

Q2 a) E.g. bathroom cleaners

b) A chemical that destroys bacteria or stops them growing.

c) They are used outside the body to help to clean wounds and surfaces, to prevent infection.

Q3 a) To defend themselves against bacteria.

b) E.g. tea tree oil

Pages 37-38 — Antiseptics and Antibiotics

Q1 a) An antibiotic is a substance that kills bacteria or fungi.

b) 9 days

c) To prevent the emergence of antibiotic resistant bacteria.

d) E.g. MRSA (methicillin-resistant *Staphylococcus aureus*)

Q2 a) Flu is caused by a virus and antibiotics do not affect viruses.

b) Bacteria can mutate — sometimes mutations cause them to be resistant to an antibiotic. If you have an infection some of the bacteria might be resistant to antibiotics. This means when you treat the infection only the non-resistant strains of bacteria will be killed. The individual resistant bacteria will survive and reproduce and the population of the resistant strain will increase.

Q3 a) Accept 3100 - 3300
b) E.g. fewer people got the disease. / More people had access to the antibiotic.
c) E.g. The microorganism causing the disease has become resistant to the antibiotic. / Fewer people are being given the antibiotic.
Q4 a) In the clear zone no bacteria have grown, because they have been killed by the antiseptic.
b) Antiseptic 3.

Pages 39-40 — Energy and Biomass

Q1 a) Plants, photosynthesis
b) eat
c) respiration
d) lost, movement
Q2 a) false
b) true
c) false
d) true
e) true
f) false
Q3 a) 3
b) Energy always decreases from one trophic level to the next.
Q4 a) C
b) It takes a lot of food from the level below to keep any one animal alive, so the amount of biomass decreases as you move up the trophic levels.
c) The energy in the nettles comes from sunlight.
d) So much energy is lost at each stage that there's not enough left to support more organisms after four or five stages.
Q5 a) Organisms depend on each other for e.g. food, pollination, shelter, in order to survive and reproduce.
b) i) They have less food.
ii) They have fewer predators / less competition for food.
iii) They are more likely to be eaten by Barn owls.

Page 41 — Parasitism and Mutualism

Q1 a) host
b) Both organisms benefit from the relationship.
Q2 Mistletoe — Grows on trees and shrubs, absorbing water and nutrients from them.
Tapeworms — Attach to an animal's intestinal wall and absorb lots of nutrients.
Fleas — Live in the fur and bedding of animals, and feed by sucking their blood.
Headlice — Live on human scalps and suck their blood, making them itch.
Q3 a) Oxpeckers get a source of food. Buffalo get pests removed and get alerted if predators are near.
b) Nitrogen-fixing bacteria get a constant supply of sugar from the plant. The legumes get essential nitrates from the bacteria.
c) Chemosynthetic bacteria are provided with a place to live and chemicals from seawater. Tubeworms get food from the bacteria.
d) Cleaner wrasses get a source of food and protection from being eaten. Groupers get parasites and dead skin removed.

Pages 42-43 — Human Activity and the Environment

Q1 a) i) They would decrease / be used up due to the increased demand for energy and goods.
ii) Waste disposal will get harder because more waste will be produced.

b) i) E.g. detergents
ii) E.g. fertilisers
iii) E.g. coal-burning power stations
Q2 a)

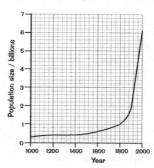

b) i) bigger
ii) faster
iii) greater
c) E.g. Improvements in medicine meant that fewer people died of diseases. More efficient farming methods produced more food so fewer people died of hunger.
Q3 a) Without them, crops wouldn't grow as well, and so food yields would be lower. Crops take nitrates out of the soil so these nitrates need to be replaced.
b) It is washed out of the soil by rainfall.
c) It causes rapid growth of algae which prevents other plants from getting enough light. Some plants then start dying due to competition for light. Bacteria feed on the dead plant material and multiply, using up the oxygen in the water. This causes the death of animals in the water by suffocation.
d) eutrophication
Q4 a) A
b) Height increased as nitrate increased, from no nitrate to high nitrate concentration. Very high nitrate concentration reduced the number and height of the plants.

Page 44 — Recycling

Q1 It uses less energy and therefore less fossil fuel. Less carbon dioxide is produced as a result.
Q2 a) It often takes less energy to recycle materials than to manufacture new materials.
b) Any three from collecting / sorting / cleaning / processing the waste to be recycled.
Q3 a) Plastics are really slow to decompose — so recycling them helps to reduce the space taken up in landfill sites.
b) Recycling paper means that fewer trees need to be felled. Trees absorb carbon dioxide from the atmosphere, reducing global warming.
OR: Recycling paper uses less energy / fossil fuel, so less carbon dioxide is added to the atmosphere, reducing global warming.

Page 45 — Indicator Species

Q1 a) Drain B
b) E.g. blood worms, freshwater shrimps

B1 Topic 3 — Inter-relationships

Q2 a)

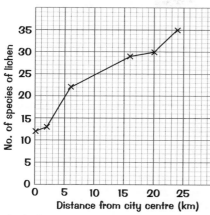

b) The further you go from the city centre, the more species of lichen there are.

c) E.g. the further you go from the city centre, the fewer cars / less industry there tends to be, so there's less sulfur dioxide in the air. Lichen grows better in clean air.

d) E.g. blackspot fungus on rose leaves

Pages 46-47 — The Carbon Cycle

Q1

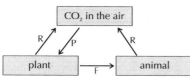

Q2 a) 1. Carbon dioxide in the air.
2. Plants take in carbon dioxide for photosynthesis and make carbon compounds.
3. Animals eat the plants' carbon compounds.
4. Plants and animals die.

b) Dead organisms are broken down by decomposers, which release carbon dioxide during respiration.

Q3 a) carbon dioxide

b) carbohydrates, protein and fats

c) By animals feeding on plants and other organisms.

d) Any three from e.g.: they can be eaten / decayed by microorganisms / turned into fossil fuels / turned into products by humans (e.g. paper).

Q4 a) fossil fuel

b) Fossil fuels come from dead animals and plants, which contain carbon.

c) combustion / burning

Q5 a) E.g. oxygen, hydrogen and nitrogen.

b) The nutrients that become part of animals and plants can only be released again by decay of the animals' or plants' dead bodies. This decay is carried out by microorganisms.

Page 48 — The Nitrogen Cycle

Q1 a) protein

b) 78%

c) an unreactive, can't

Q2 Plants — From nitrates in the soil
Animals — By eating other organisms
Bacteria in soil — By breaking down dead organisms and animal waste

Q3 a) Decompose proteins and urea into ammonia.

b) Turn ammonia in decaying matter into nitrates which plants can use.

c) Turn nitrogen gas into nitrogen compounds that plants can use.

Q4 a) Nitrifying bacteria converting ammonia into nitrates.

b) Denitrifying bacteria converting nitrates in the soil into nitrogen gas.

c) It makes nitrogen react with oxygen in the air to give nitrates.

Q5 Legume plants have root nodules that contain nitrogen-fixing bacteria. These bacteria convert nitrogen gas into nitrogen compounds, increasing the fertility of the soil.

Pages 49-52 — Mixed Questions — B1 Topic 3

Q1 a) protozoan, mosquitoes, biting, vector

b) a chemical that can lead to cancer

c) i) a depressant

ii) It decreases the activity of the brain, which slows down the responses of the nervous system.

Q2 a) A disease-causing microorganism.

b) E.g. bacteria, protozoa, fungi, viruses.

c) They live off the host, and take what they need to survive without giving anything in return.

d) The respiratory tract is lined with mucus and cilia. The mucus catches dust and bacteria before they reach the lungs and the cilia push the mucus away from the lungs.

Q3 a) all three

b) carbon monoxide

c) sulfur dioxide

d) carbon dioxide

Q4 a) Nitrates.

b) Nitrogen gas is very unreactive so it can't be turned directly into other compounds by plants.

c) Both organisms benefit from the relationship.
The plants get nitrogen compounds from the bacteria, and the bacteria get sugars from the plants.

Q5 a) Using non-living indicators means using electronic meters or doing chemical tests on a sample of air to find the concentration of pollutants in it. Using living indicators means observing the organisms that are sensitive to changes in their environment, e.g. lichens, blackspot fungi.

b) Town A is the more polluted, as fewer lichens are able to survive in polluted air. (Clean air usually leads to more organisms in total and a greater variety of species.)

Q6 a) the Sun

b) E.g. in maintaining a constant body temperature, egestion.

c) A — respiration
B — feeding / ingestion / digestion
C — decomposition / decay
D — respiration by decomposers
E — photosynthesis
F — respiration

d)

Q7 a) a fungus

b) By contact with contaminated surfaces, e.g. the skin of an infected person or shower floors and towels used by an infected person.

c) i) ethanol

ii) B

iii) D

iv) E.g. temperature / size of the discs / concentration of the plant extract

C1a Topic 1 — The Earth's Sea and Atmosphere

C1a Topic 1 — The Earth's Sea and Atmosphere

Pages 53-54 — The Evolution of the Atmosphere

Q1　True statements: When the Earth was formed, its surface was molten.
When some plants died and were buried under layers of sediment, the carbon they had removed from the atmosphere became locked up in carbonate rocks.

Q2　The percentage of carbon dioxide has decreased by a large amount because it dissolved into the oceans and green plants used it for photosynthesis.

Q3　The statements should be in this order (from the top of the timeline):
1. The atmosphere is about four-fifths nitrogen and one-fifth oxygen.
2. The build-up of oxygen in the atmosphere allows more complex organisms to evolve and flourish.
The oxygen also creates the ozone layer.
3. Green plants evolve over most of the Earth. They're quite happy in the CO_2 atmosphere. A lot of the CO_2 dissolves into the oceans. The green plants also absorb some of the CO_2 and produce O_2 by photosynthesis.
4. Water vapour condenses to form oceans.
5. The Earth cools down slightly. A thin crust forms. There's lots of volcanic activity.
6. The Earth's surface is molten — it's so hot that any atmosphere just 'boils away' into space.

Q4 a)　Largest sector is Nitrogen, second largest is Oxygen, smallest is Carbon dioxide and other gases.

b)　Nitrogen: 80% approx (to be more precise, it's 78% in dry air)
Oxygen: 20% approx (to be more precise, it's 21% in dry air)

c)　Nitrogen has increased. Carbon dioxide has decreased. Far less water vapour now. Oxygen is now a significant proportion of the atmosphere.

d)　As the planet cooled, the water vapour condensed and formed the oceans.

e)　Plants and microorganisms photosynthesised and produced it.

f)　In any order:
Created the ozone layer which blocked harmful rays from the Sun.
Killed off early organisms/allowed more complex ones to evolve.

Page 55 — Today's Atmosphere

Q1 a) i)　One of: burning fossil fuels / deforestation
ii)　One of:
Burning fossil fuels releases carbon dioxide into the atmosphere, causing the level to rise. /
Deforestation means there are fewer trees removing carbon dioxide by photosynthesis.

b)　Generally increased, although it has fluctuated.

c)　No-one was around millions of years ago so we are making guesses based upon evidence like bubbles of air trapped in ice.

Q2　About 40 cm³. Air is 20% oxygen so about 10 cm³ would be used in the reaction (20% of 50), leaving 40 cm³.

C1a Topic 2 — Materials from the Earth

Pages 56-57 — The Three Different Types of Rock

Q1　igneous rocks — formed when magma cools — granite
metamorphic rocks — formed under intense heat and pressure — marble
sedimentary rocks — formed from layers of sediment — limestone

Q2　Crust, slowly, big, intrusive, quickly, small, extrusive

Q3 a)　E.g. the church is made from limestone which is formed mostly from sea shells.

b)　The pressure forces out the water. Fluids flowing through the pores deposit minerals that cement the sediment together.

c)　They are both made from the same chemical.

Q4 a)　1. Possible uplift to the surface
2. Pressure from rocks above
3. Metamorphic rocks forming here
4. Intense heat from below

b)　Metamorphic rock has a hard, even texture.

Q5 a)　True

b)　False. They are formed over millions of years.

c)　False. Chalk is a sedimentary rock.

d)　False. Igneous rocks are harder.

e)　True

Q6　Limestone and chalk are sedimentary rocks which aren't formed at high temperatures, so the fossils aren't destroyed by heat.

Pages 58-60 — Using Limestone

Q1　glass, cement and concrete

Q2 a)　Any two from: noise, dust, loss of habitats for plants and animals, increased traffic and noise / pollution from lorries.

b)　Quarries provide employment for local people which can provide a boost to the local economy. There may also be improvements to infrastructure such as roads, recreational and health facilities.

Q3 a)　neutralisation

b)　The limestone removes sulfur dioxide from the smoke emitted from the power stations. This helps to reduce acid rain.

Q4 a)　The limestone in the Peak District is very pure.

b)　About 1.6 million tonnes ($7.9 \div 5 = 1.58$).

c)　It is used in agriculture and burned in lime kilns.

d) i)　canals and railways
ii)　by road / by lorry

e)　Answer will depend on student's opinion, but they are likely to say that they are against it because the article focuses on the problems associated with quarrying rather than the benefits it has.

f)

Use	Percentage	Total amount quarried in tonnes
Aggregate (for road-building etc.)	52%	$(7900000 \div 100) \times 52 = 4108000$
Cement	24%	$(7900000 \div 100) \times 24 = 1896000$
Iron and steel making	2%	$(7900000 \div 100) \times 2 = 158000$
Chemicals and other uses	22%	$(7900000 \div 100) \times 22 = 1738000$

C1a Topic 2 — Materials from the Earth

Pages 61-62 — Limestone and Thermal Decomposition

Q1 a) Thermal decomposition is when one substance chemically changes into at least two new substances when it's heated.
b) Calcium oxide will react with water to give an alkaline substance. You could prove this using universal indicator (it would turn blue or purple). Calcium carbonate would remain neutral.
c) Pass the gas produced through limewater. The limewater will go cloudy/milk/white, proving that carbon dioxide is present.
Q2 a) calcium carbonate
b) calcium oxide, carbon dioxide
c) zinc oxide
d) copper carbonate → copper oxide + carbon dioxide
Q3 a) calcium carbonate → calcium oxide + carbon dioxide
b) To neutralise soils that are acidic.
Q4 a) 1. Heat the carbonate in a boiling tube.
2. Pipe off the gas into a test tube of limewater.
3. Record the time taken for the limewater to change colour.
4. Repeat for each carbonate.
5. Compare your results.
b)

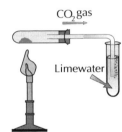

CO$_2$ gas

Limewater

c) i) The limewater would turn milky more quickly for the carbonate that decomposed the fastest.
ii) Some carbonates are more stable than others. Less stable carbonates decompose more readily.
d) A colour change, as some carbonates are a different colour to their oxides.

Page 63 — Atoms and Mass in Chemical Reactions

Q1 atoms, particles, atoms, rearranged, mass, constant.
Q2 a) A precipitate is an insoluble solid that forms in a solution.
b) copper sulfate + sodium hydroxide → copper hydroxide + sodium sulfate
c) 27 g (12 g + 15 g)
Q3 a) 11 g (29 g – 18 g)
b) yes

Pages 64-65 — Balancing Equations

Q1 a) Correctly balanced
b) Incorrectly balanced
c) Incorrectly balanced
d) Correctly balanced
e) Correctly balanced
Q2 The third equation should be circled.
Q3 a) The reactants are methane and oxygen, and the products are carbon dioxide and water.
b) methane + oxygen → carbon dioxide + water
c) $CH_4 + 2O_2 \rightarrow CO_2 + 2H_2O$
Q4 a) $2Na + Cl_2 \rightarrow 2NaCl$
b) $4Li + O_2 \rightarrow 2Li_2O$
c) $MgCO_3 + 2HCl \rightarrow MgCl_2 + H_2O + CO_2$
d) $2Li + 2H_2O \rightarrow 2LiOH + H_2$

Q5 a) $CuO + 2HBr \rightarrow CuBr_2 + H_2O$
b) $H_2 + Br_2 \rightarrow 2HBr$
c) $2Mg + O_2 \rightarrow 2MgO$
d) $2NaOH + H_2SO_4 \rightarrow Na_2SO_4 + 2H_2O$
Q6 a) $3NaOH + AlBr_3 \rightarrow 3NaBr + Al(OH)_3$
b) $2FeCl_2 + Cl_2 \rightarrow 2FeCl_3$
c) $N_2 + 3H_2 \rightarrow 2NH_3$
d) $4Fe + 3O_2 \rightarrow 2Fe_2O_3$
e) $4NH_3 + 5O_2 \rightarrow 4NO + 6H_2O$

Pages 66-68 — Mixed Questions — C1a Topics 1 & 2

Q1 a) i)

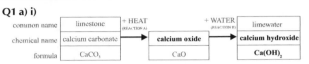

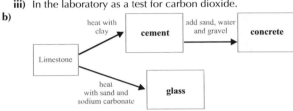

ii) $CaCO_3 \rightarrow CaO + CO_2$
iii) In the laboratory as a test for carbon dioxide.
b)

Limestone —heat with clay→ cement —add sand, water and gravel→ concrete

Limestone —heat with sand and sodium carbonate→ glass

c) Acid rain reacts with the limestone and causes it to dissolve.
d) i) Limestone is turned into marble when very high temperatures break it down over a long period of time. The limestone reforms as small crystals.
ii) 1. Marble has a more even texture and is harder than limestone.
2. Unlike limestone, marble doesn't usually contain fossils. The high temperature it is formed at destroys them.
Q2 a) No. There was virtually no oxygen so today's complex organisms couldn't survive.
b) green plants
c) increasing, carbon dioxide, burning, reduces, absorbed.
d) i) False, only 1% of the atmosphere is noble gases.
ii) True
iii) False, plants take in carbon dioxide and give out oxygen during photosynthesis.
e) No-one was around millions of years ago so we can only make guesses and theories.
Q3 a) s
b) l
c) g
d) aq
Q4 a) $ZnCO_3 \rightarrow ZnO + CO_2$
b) $2Cu + O_2 \rightarrow 2CuO$
c) $CaO + H_2O \rightarrow Ca(OH)_2$
Q5 a) Place the reactants in a flask sealed with a bung. React copper sulfate with sodium hydroxide to produce a precipitate of copper hydroxide in sodium sulfate. Weigh at the start and end of the reaction. Compare the two measurements — there should be no change in mass.
b) Thermal decomposition of carbonates produces carbon dioxide gas. If the apparatus was not sealed this product would escape, and so it would seem as though the reaction mass had changed.
c) No atoms are lost or gained. They are just rearranged.

C1b Topic 3 — Acids

C1b Topic 3 — Acids

Page 69 — Hazard Symbols

Q1 a) false
b) true
c) false
d) true
e) false
f) false
g) true

Q2 a) — corrosive — attacks and destroys living tissue.

b) — irritant — causes reddening or blistering of the skin.

c) — toxic — can cause death if swallowed, inhaled or absorbed through the skin.

d) — oxidising — provides oxygen which allows other materials to burn more fiercely.

e) — harmful — like toxic but not quite as dangerous.

f) — highly flammable — catches fire easily.

Page 70 — Acids and Alkalis

Q1 a) acidic
b) acid
c) base
d) water
e) 7
Q2 a) purple — 14 — strong alkali
b) yellow — 5/6 — weak acid
c) dark green/blue — 8/9 — weak alkali
d) red — 1 — strong acid
e) green — 7 — neutral
Q3 a) Baking soda or soap powder, because they are weak bases and so would neutralise the acid but wouldn't irritate or harm the skin. Stronger bases like caustic soda might damage the skin.
b) E.g. the colour can be difficult to judge exactly.

Page 71 — Hydrochloric Acid and Indigestion Tablets

Q1 Missing words are: digestion, acidic, kill, too much, base, neutralise.
Q2 a) B — 15.9, C — 23.4, D —16.7, E — 6.6
b) Tablet E
c) Tablet E
d) Tablet C is most effective because a single dose neutralises the largest volume of acid.

Pages 72-75 — Reactions of Acids

Q1 acid + metal hydroxide → salt + water
Q2 acid + metal oxide → salt + water
Q3 a) hydrochloric acid + lead oxide → **lead** chloride + water
b) nitric acid + copper hydroxide → copper **nitrate** + water
c) sulfuric acid + zinc oxide → zinc sulfate + **water**
d) hydrochloric acid + **nickel** oxide → nickel **chloride** + **water**
e) **nitric** acid + copper oxide → **copper** nitrate + **water**
f) sulfuric acid + **sodium** hydroxide → sodium **sulfate** + **water**
g) hydrochloric acid + **calcium** hydroxide → calcium **chloride** + **water**

Q4 a) $CuO_{(s)}$
b) $H_2O_{(l)}$
c) $HCl_{(aq)}$
d) $ZnO_{(s)}$
e) $Na_2SO_{4(aq)} + 2H_2O_{(l)}$
f) $KNO_{3\ (aq)} + H_2O_{(l)}$
g) $H_2SO_{4\ (aq)}, H_2O_{(l)}$
Q5 a) $H_3PO_4 + 3NaOH \rightarrow Na_3PO_4 + 3H_2O$
b) $2NaOH + H_2SO_4 \rightarrow Na_2SO_4 + 2H_2O$
c) $Mg(OH)_2 + 2HNO_3 \rightarrow Mg(NO_3)_2 + 2H_2O$
d) $2NH_3 + H_2SO_4 \rightarrow (NH_4)_2SO_4$
Q6 acid + metal carbonate → salt + water + carbon dioxide
Q7 a) nitric acid + sodium carbonate → **sodium nitrate** + **carbon dioxide** + **water**
b) calcium carbonate + hydrochloric acid → **calcium chloride** + **carbon dioxide** + **water**
c) **zinc carbonate** + sulfuric acid → zinc sulfate + **carbon dioxide** + **water**
d) nitric acid + **magnesium carbonate** → magnesium nitrate + **carbon dioxide** + **water**
e) copper carbonate + **hydrochloric acid** → copper chloride + **carbon dioxide** + **water**
f) **magnesium carbonate** + **sulfuric acid** → magnesium sulfate + **carbon dioxide** + **water**
Q8 a) chloride
b) nitrate
c) sulfate
Q9 a) $CuCO_{3(s)}$
b) $MgCO_{3(s)}, CO_{2(g)}$
c) $ZnCO_{3(s)}$
d) $Na_2SO_{4(aq)} + H_2O_{(l)} + CO_{2(g)}$
Q10 a) $2HCl + CaCO_3 \rightarrow CaCl_2 + H_2O + CO_2$
b) $2HCl + K_2CO_3 \rightarrow 2KCl + H_2O + CO_2$
c) $2HNO_3 + ZnCO_3 \rightarrow Zn(NO_3)_2 + H_2O + CO_2$
d) $Na_2CO_3 + 2HCl \rightarrow 2NaCl + H_2O + CO_2$

Pages 76-77 — Electrolysis

Q1 Missing words are: electrical energy, direct current, electrolyte, electrodes, gas.
Q2 a) Hydrogen and chlorine
b) Hydrogen gives a 'squeaky pop' when it comes into contact with a burning splint.
Chlorine bleaches damp litmus paper.
Q3 a) Chlorine gas was produced in the experiment, and it is also used to kill bacteria in swimming pools.
b) Chlorine gas is toxic.
c) The experiment should be carried out in a fume cupboard / The lab should be checked to make sure it is well ventilated.
Q4 a) chlorine
b) $100 - (11 + 20 + 6 + 5 + 33) = 25\%$
c) plastics
Q5 a) hydrogen and oxygen
b) He would test the gases to show that they're oxygen and hydrogen, and that there's no chlorine present. The hydrogen will make a 'squeaky pop' with a lighted splint. Oxygen will relight a glowing splint. Oxygen isn't produced by the electrolysis of hydrochloric acid. He could also do the chlorine test on the gases. If neither bleaches damp litmus paper then chlorine isn't present. These tests would prove that he wasn't using hydrochloric acid.

C1b Topic 4 — Obtaining and Using Metals

C1b Topic 4 — Obtaining and Using Metals

Page 78 — Metal Ores

Q1 a) True
b) True
c) False
d) True

Q2 Carbon (in the wood) is more reactive than copper, so it 'steals' oxygen from the copper ore.

Q3 Carbon, below, reduction, electrolysis, more

Q4 a) It is unreactive so doesn't tend to form compounds with other elements.
b) i) $3Fe + 2O_2 \rightarrow Fe_3O_4$
ii) oxidised
c) i) $2CuO + C \rightarrow 2Cu + CO_2$
ii) reduced

Pages 79-80 — Reduction of Metal Ores

Q1 a) Iron is lower in the reactivity series than carbon so carbon will displace iron from its oxide.
b) iron(III) oxide + carbon → iron + carbon dioxide
c) $2Fe_2O_3 + 3C \rightarrow 4Fe + 3CO_2$
d) Potassium, Magnesium, Calcium, Aluminium and Sodium should be ticked.

Q2 a) Name: sphalerite/zinc sulfide, chemical formula: ZnS
b) zinc sulfide + oxygen → zinc oxide + sulfur dioxide
c) $2ZnO + C \rightarrow 2Zn + CO_2$

Q3 Electrolysis — The breakdown of a substance using electricity.
Electrolyte — The liquid that is used in electrolysis.
Electrode — Used to apply electricity to the liquid.

Q4 a) True
b) True
c) False
d) False
e) False

Q5 A — d.c. source
B — electrode
C — molten aluminium oxide
D — molten aluminium

Pages 81-82 — Properties of Metals

Q1 a) Metal 3 (because it has the best heat conduction, and is strong and resistant to corrosion).
b) Metal 2 (because it is the strongest, isn't too expensive and won't corrode too much). (Accept metal 3.)
c) Metal 1 (because it is most resistant to corrosion so it will last a long time).

Q2 Desirable qualities in a metal used to make knives and forks would be: e.g. strong, resistant to corrosion, visually attractive / shiny, non-toxic.

Q3 a) low density
b) conducts heat
c) resists corrosion
d) ductile

Q4 a) A and B
b) A, because it took least time for the end that wasn't near the heat source to heat up.

Q5 Any three from: good conductor of electricity, good conductor of heat, strong, easily bendable.

Q6 Missing words are: some, oxidised, more, easily, less

Pages 83-84 — Making Metals More Useful

Q1 a) A mixture of two or more metals or a mixture of a metal and a non-metal.
b) By adding small amounts of carbon and sometimes other metals to the iron.

Q2 low-carbon steel — 0.1% carbon — car bodies
high-carbon steel — 1.5% carbon — blades for tools
stainless steel — chromium — cutlery

Q3 a) nickel, titanium
b) zinc, copper or nickel
c) gold

Q4 a) 37.5% (9 ÷ 24 x 100 = 37.5)
b) 9-carat gold is harder than pure gold because it is an alloy and so it contains different sized atoms. The atoms in 9-carat gold can't slide over each other as easily as the ones in pure gold can.

Q5 a) Fineness means the number of parts of pure gold per thousand.
b) 900 fineness is the same as — 90% pure gold.
042 fineness is the same as — 1 carat gold.
375 fineness is the same as — 9 carat gold.
750 fineness is the same as — a gold alloy with 25% other metals.

Q6 a) Any sensible answer, e.g. for making spectacle frames.
b) i) They have a shape memory property.
ii) They have an ability to return to their original shape if they have been bent out of shape.

Page 85 — Recycling

Q1 E.g. any three from: Recycling means using less finite resources.
Recycling uses a fraction of the energy that mining, extracting and purifying the original metal would.
Using less energy means recycling can also be cheaper than making more of the original material.
Recycling means less rubbish has to be put into landfill, which takes up space and pollutes the surroundings.

Q2 a) True
b) True
c) False

Q3 a) i) 4 × 1 = **4 tonnes**.
ii) 3 billion × 20 = **60 billion g of aluminium**
60 billion ÷ 1000 = **60 million kg of aluminium**
60 million ÷ 1000 = **60 000 tonnes of aluminium**
iii) about 60 000 × 4 = **240 000 tonnes of bauxite**
b) i) Mining the bauxite causes deforestation, as the mines are often located in rainforests in addition to the general pollution and damage to the landscape associated with mining.
ii) Large amounts of electricity are needed to extract the aluminium, which means a lot of fossil fuel has to be burned. This generates a lot of CO_2, adding to the greenhouse effect.
iii) This means more bauxite has to be mined and the aluminium extracted, destroying more rainforest and producing more CO_2. The waste cans would also increase the amount of landfill.

C1b Topic 5 — Fuels

C1b Topic 5 — Fuels

Pages 86-87 — Fractional Distillation of Crude Oil

Q1 a) Crude oil is a **mixture** of different molecules.
b) Crude oil contains **hydrocarbon** molecules.
c) The molecules in crude oil **aren't** chemically bonded to each other.
d) Physical methods **can** be used to separate out the molecules in crude oil.
Q2 hydrogen and carbon
Q3

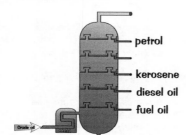

Q4 The larger the molecule the higher the boiling/condensing point.
Q5 Gas: Used for cooking and heating
Petrol: Used as a fuel for cars
Kerosene: Used as an aircraft fuel
Diesel Oil: Used as a fuel for lorries, trains and some cars
Fuel Oil: Used as a fuel for ships and some power stations
Bitumen: Used to surface roads and roofs
Q6 lower, carbon/hydrogen, hydrogen/carbon, ignite, viscous
Q7 Crude oil is a finite resource and will one day run out. This means that petrol will run out too.

Page 88 — Burning Fuels

Q1 a) hydrocarbon + oxygen → carbon dioxide + water
b) oxidised, gives out
Q2 Any three from:
E.g. how easily it burns / its energy value / how much ash or smoke it produces / how easy it is to store or transport.
Q3 a) CO_2 and H_2O
b) If there is not enough oxygen.
Q4 a) hydrocarbon + oxygen → **carbon** + **carbon monoxide** + **carbon dioxide** + **water**
b) Carbon monoxide is produced which is a very toxic (poisonous) gas.

Page 89 — Environmental Problems

Q1 Hydrocarbon fuels like petrol and diesel often contain impurities of sulfur. When they are burnt, sulfur dioxide gas is released into the air.
Q2 The main cause of acid rain is sulfur dioxide.
Acid rain kills trees and acidifies lakes.
Limestone buildings and statues are affected by acid rain.
In clouds sulfur dioxide reacts with water to make sulfuric acid.
Q3 Any three from:
E.g. removing the sulfur from the fuel before it is burnt (using low-sulfur fuels).
Fitting cars with catalytic converters.
Using scrubbers in power station chimneys to remove sulfur dioxide from emissions.
Reducing the usage of fossil fuels.

Q4 Answer will depend on student's opinion — may argue that everyone who lives on Earth and uses its resources has a responsibility to try and prevent environmental damage. Alternatively, may suggest that new technologies will be able to prevent damage.

Pages 90-91 — More Environmental Problems

Q1 True statements:
Greenhouse gases include carbon dioxide and methane.
Increasing amounts of greenhouse gases are causing global warming.
Q2 a) Global temperature has generally increased, although it has fluctuated.
b) E.g. burning fossil fuels and deforestation
c) E.g. the graph shows data collected over a long time to show that the temperature change is not just a temporary fluctuation.
Q3 fossil, an increase, CO_2, greenhouse
Q4 a) C
b) i) Cars burn fossil fuels and give out CO_2 in their exhaust gases.
ii) The TV uses up electricity so the power station has to burn more fuel, which produces CO_2.
Q5 a) False
b) True
c) False
Q6 a) seeding, injecting, phytoplankton, photosynthesis, hydrocarbons, high
b) Any one from:
E.g. there is no way of controlling what plankton grows — some is toxic.
When the plankton dies it is decomposed by microorganisms that use up oxygen, creating 'dead zones' in the ocean.
If carbon dioxide isn't converted into hydrocarbons using 'green' energy then this process just increases CO_2 levels.

Pages 92-93 — Biofuels

Q1 Biofuels are alternatives to fossil fuels. They're made from chemicals obtained from living things, e.g. living organisms' waste or dead plants.
Q2 a)

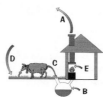

b) The plants used to produce biogas can be replaced with new plants, and the animal waste will constantly be replaced by the animals or by new animals.
c) Biogas is a cheap fuel because the raw materials (plant waste or manure) are cheap and readily available.
Q3 a) True
b) True
c) False
d) False
e) False
Q4 a) water and carbon dioxide
b) The crops needed for its production absorb CO_2 from the atmosphere in photosynthesis while growing.
c) The weather in Britain is not as good and there is not as much available land for crop growth as there is in Brazil.
Q5 a) Advantages could include:
renewable, fewer particulates emitted, don't cause acid rain, don't add as much CO_2 to the atmosphere, raw materials are cheap/readily available.

C1b Topic 5 — Fuels

b) Disadvantages could include:
can be unreliable (e.g. sugar crop for ethanol may fail),
can require large amounts of land to grow the plants /
keep the animals, CO_2 is still emitted when the fuels are
burned, distilling the ethanol uses a lot of energy.

Page 94 — Fuel Cells

Q1 a)   Oxygen: Relights a glowing splint
Hydrogen: Makes a squeaky pop when burnt
b)   water
Q2   fuel, oxygen, electricity
Q3   Advantages could include:
They're more efficient than batteries and power stations.
There are no moving parts unlike in a car engine or power
station so energy isn't lost through friction.
The only by-products are water and heat so there are no
pollutants produced. Unlike batteries they don't run down
or need recharging. Unlike batteries they aren't polluting
to dispose of.
Disadvantages could include:
Hydrogen is a gas so it takes up loads more space to store
than liquid fuels like petrol. It's difficult to store safely.
The hydrogen fuel is often made either from hydrocarbons
(from fossil fuels), or by electrolysis of water which uses
electricity (usually generated using fossil fuels).

Page 95 — Measuring the Energy Content of Fuels

Q1 a)

Fuel	Initial Mass (g)	Final Mass (g)	Mass of Fuel Burnt (g)
A	98	92	6
B	102	89	13

b) i)   fuel A
ii)   It takes less fuel to heat the water by the same amount.
c) i)

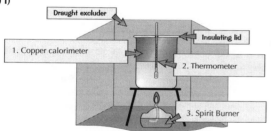

1. Copper calorimeter
2. Thermometer
3. Spirit Burner
Draught excluder
Insulating lid

ii)   To reduce heat loss.
d)   E.g.
1. The apparatus
2. The amount of water
3. The start and finish temperatures of the water

Page 96 — Alkanes and Alkenes

Q1 a)   ethene
b)

H–C–C–H (with H H above and H H below)

c)   methane
Q2 a)   False
b)   True
c)   False
d)   True
e)   True
Q3   bromine water, decolourise, bromine water, brown,
colourless

Page 97 — Cracking Hydrocarbons

Q1   shorter, petrol, diesel, long, high, catalyst,
molecules, cracking, alkenes
Q2 a)   On the mineral wool.
b)   The porcelain acts as a catalyst.
c)   Small alkanes and alkenes.
Q3 $C_{10}H_{22} \rightarrow C_8H_{18} + C_2H_4$

Pages 98-99 — Using Alkenes to Make Polymers

Q1 a)   ethene
b)

$$n \begin{pmatrix} CH_3\ H \\ |\quad\ | \\ C = C \\ |\quad\ | \\ H\quad H \end{pmatrix} \longrightarrow \begin{pmatrix} CH_3\ H \\ |\quad\ | \\ C - C \\ |\quad\ | \\ H\quad H \end{pmatrix}_n$$

Q2 a)

C=C with H, Cl above and H, H below

b)

$$n \begin{pmatrix} H\quad\ Cl \\ C=C \\ H\quad\ H \end{pmatrix} \rightarrow \begin{pmatrix} H\ Cl \\ |\ \ | \\ C-C \\ |\ \ | \\ H\ H \end{pmatrix}_n$$

Q3   Poly(ethene) — Plastic bags
Poly(propene) — Carpets, thermal underwear and plastic
containers
PVC — Clothing, electric cables and pipes
PTFE — Non-stick coating for pans
Q4   Cracking is the breakdown of large molecules into smaller
ones, whereas polymerisation is small molecules joining to
form bigger molecules.
Cracking makes small alkenes and alkanes, polymerisation
often uses alkenes to make alkanes.
Cracking usually involves breaking single bonds between
carbon atoms. In polymerisation, the double bonds in
carbon atoms are broken.
Q5 a)   Waste remains in landfill. Landfill sites are getting full and
more are needed, which takes up useful land.
b)   They produce toxic gases when burnt.
c)   E.g. recycling is expensive.
There are lots of types of plastic and they need to be
separated out before recycling.
d)   The polymer could break down into products that are
harmful.

Pages 100-104 — Mixed Questions — C1b Topics 3, 4 & 5

Q1 a)   The following should be ticked:
Metals are generally strong but also bendy.
Metals corrode when they are oxidised.
Properties of a metal can be altered by mixing it with
another metal to form an alloy.
b) i)   E.g. copper is below hydrogen in the reactivity series, and
so it doesn't react with water.
ii)   E.g. gold is used for jewellery because it is shiny / gold
is used in electric circuits/tooth fillings because it is
unreactive.
c)   R. The material needs to be as light and as strong as
possible with a high melting point and a reasonable price.
S has a low melting point. T is expensive and fairly dense.
U is not very strong and has a high density.
Q2 a)   Dead plant material.
b)   The CO_2 released when biogas is burnt is balanced out by
the CO_2 removed from the atmosphere when the plants
photosynthesised.

P1a Topic 1 — Visible Light and the Solar System

Q3 a) A finite resource is a resource of which there's a limited amount, which cannot be replenished.
b) i) In general, the more reactive the metal, the later it was discovered.
  ii) Less reactive metals are easier to extract from their ores, for example by reduction with carbon. The least reactive metals are sometimes found uncombined in nature.
c) i) iron(III) oxide + **carbon** → iron + **carbon dioxide**
  ii) $2Fe_2O_3 + 3C \rightarrow 4Fe + 3CO_2$
d) Any two from: easily bent, ductile/easily drawn into wires, high melting point, good conductor of electricity.
e) i) bauxite
  ii) Aluminium is more reactive than carbon, and so cannot be extracted by reduction with carbon.
Q4 a) E.g.
  1. Petrol has a lower boiling point than diesel.
  2. Petrol is more flammable (ignites more easily) than diesel.
b) i) E.g. by the fermentation of plants
  ii) When it's burnt, there are fewer pollutants than from petrol or diesel. / The CO_2 released when ethanol is burnt is balanced out by the CO_2 the plants took in during photosynthesis.
Q5 a) E.g. carbon dioxide is given off which is a greenhouse gas / sulfur dioxide is given off which causes acid rain.
b) E.g. bitumen for surfacing roads
Q6 a) electrolysis
b) i) hydrogen and oxygen
  ii) Hydrogen gives a squeaky pop when lit. Oxygen relights a glowing splint.
Q7 a)

$$H-\underset{\underset{H}{|}}{\overset{\overset{H}{|}}{C}}-\underset{\underset{H}{|}}{\overset{\overset{H}{|}}{C}}=C\overset{H}{\underset{H}{\diagdown}}$$

b) Alkanes have no double C=C bond but alkenes do.
Q8 a) cracking
b) E.g. decane → propene + heptane
  $C_{10}H_{22} \rightarrow C_3H_6 + C_7H_{16}$
Q9 a) Lots of small molecules (monomers) join up to make long chain molecules (polymers).
b) Name: poly(chloroethene)

$$--\underset{\underset{H}{|}}{\overset{\overset{H}{|}}{C}}-\underset{\underset{Cl}{|}}{\overset{\overset{H}{|}}{C}}-\underset{\underset{H}{|}}{\overset{\overset{H}{|}}{C}}-\underset{\underset{Cl}{|}}{\overset{\overset{H}{|}}{C}}-\underset{\underset{H}{|}}{\overset{\overset{H}{|}}{C}}-\underset{\underset{Cl}{|}}{\overset{\overset{H}{|}}{C}}--$$

c) E.g. it's difficult to get rid of them. / They fill up landfill sites.
Q10 a) i) acidic
  ii) alkaline
b) Milk of magnesia is alkaline, so it can neutralise the excess acid that causes indigestion.
Q11 a) i) magnesium chloride
  ii) neutralisation
b) sulfuric acid / H_2SO_4
c) Metal oxides and metal hydroxides are usually **bases**.
Q12 a) calcium carbonate + hydrochloric acid → calcium chloride + water + carbon dioxide
b) By bubbling the gas produced through a delivery tube into limewater. The limewater would turn cloudy to show the presence of CO_2.

P1a Topic 1 — Visible Light and the Solar System

Pages 105-106 — Changing Ideas About the Solar System

Q1 a) i) True
  ii) False
  iii) False
  iv) True
b) ii) E.g. we can observe stars because they give out visible light, and we can observe planets because they **reflect** visible light.
  iii) E.g. we can observe visible light from the Universe using telescopes, the **naked eye** and **photography**.
Q2 Naked-eye observations — Only really useful for mapping positions, e.g. stars.
  Earth-based telescopes — Can be used to magnify images.
  Earth-based telescopes — Allows distant objects to be seen in more detail.
  Earth-based telescope and Naked-eye observations — Observations can be made more difficult by light pollution and the Earth's atmosphere.
Q3 E.g. any three from:
  It makes it easier to monitor an object by taking pictures over a period of time./It makes it easier to compare/share observations./You can observe faint objects by taking photos using long exposure times.
Q4 The Sun, moon, planets and stars all orbit the Earth in perfect circles.

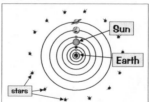

Q5 a) i) planets, Sun
  ii) circles
  iii) Sun
b) E.g. Our current model states that the Sun is not the centre of the Universe. / In the current model of the Solar System, the orbits are elliptical rather than circular like in the heliocentric model.
c) Telescopes help us look further into space which means we can make new discoveries, e.g. planets. This shows us that our Solar System and the Universe is much bigger than we originally thought. This helps disprove the idea that everything in the Universe orbits the Earth or Sun.
Q6 a) He saw four 'stars' moving around Jupiter in a different direction to what you'd expect. These 'stars' never moved away from Jupiter and seemed to be carried along with the planet. He realised they weren't stars, but moons.
b) Galileo's observations showed the moons around Jupiter were actually orbiting it. This proved that not everything was in orbit around the Earth. This showed that the geocentric model was wrong.

Pages 107-108 — Waves — Basic Principles

Q1 all, energy, matter
Q2 Transverse — 2, Longitudinal — 1.
Q3 Longitudinal: ultrasound, birdsong, drumbeat, 'push-pull' wave on a slinky, P waves.
  Transverse: electromagnetic (EM), sunlight, 'shake' wave on a slinky, S waves.
Q4 a) A and C
b) A and B
c) A and C

P1a Topic 1 — Visible Light and the Solar System

Q5   Use v = x / t = 12 / 5 = **2.4 m/s**.
Q6 a) 2 Hz
b)   The next crest is one wavelength away.
         So use v = f × λ to find λ:
         0.5 = 2 × λ.
         λ = 0.5 / 2 = **0.25 m** (or 25 cm).
Q7   v = f × λ
         $3 \times 10^8 = f \times 5 \times 10^{-7}$
         $f = (3 \times 10^8) \div (5 \times 10^{-7})$
         f = **6×10^{14} Hz**
Q8 a) 2 cm
b)   3
c)   0.01 s
Q9 a) the same direction
b)   The number of complete vibrations to and fro passing a
         point per second.

Page 109 — Reflection and Refraction

Q1 a) A normal line is a line drawn at 90 degrees to a surface,
         at the point that an incident ray reaches a surface.
b)

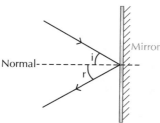

Q2   Refraction is caused by light changing speed as it enters
         another medium.
Q3 a) Nearer to her.
b)   Light travels faster in air than in water.
Q4 a) Medium 1 is **air** and medium 2 is **glass**.
b)   Light travels faster in air than in glass, so it'll bend towards
         the normal as it passes into glass.

Pages 110-111 — Lenses

Q1 a) W = incident
         X = converging
         Y = parallel
         Z = focal point
b)   The following statements should be ticked:
         Any ray passing along the axis
         Any ray passing through the centre of the lens
Q2

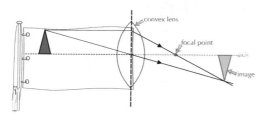

Q3

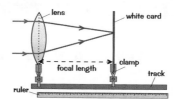

Set up the equipment as above. The lens should be
directed at a distant object, e.g. a nearby building. Turn
off any lights to make the image more visible. Move the
card along the track until you get a focused image on the
white card. Clamp the card in place and then measure the
distance from the centre of the lens to the card. This will
be the focal length of the lens.

Q4 a) E.g. the experiment will require lens, track, clamps, white
         card, object, ruler, lamp.
         Clamp the lens to a track. Clamp the card and object
         on either side — make sure the object is well lit and the
         card isn't (to make the image easier to see). Move the
         object away from the lens and move the card until you
         get a focussed image of the object on it. Use the ruler to
         measure the distance from the object to the lens, and the
         lens to the card. Record what the image is like. Repeat
         with the object at different distances.
b)

Distance from lens to object	Distance from lens to image	Type of image	Size of image
Greater than 2F	Between 2F and F	Real, inverted	Smaller than object
Equal to 2F	**Equal to 2F**	Real, inverted	**Equal to object**
Between 2F and F	Greater than 2F	**Real, inverted**	**Larger than object**
Less than F	Greater than 2F	**Virtual, upright**	Larger than object

c) i) The image will be 1 cm high.
ii) The image will be 5 cm away from the lens on the
         opposite side from the object.

Page 112 — Simple and Reflecting Telescopes

Q1a)

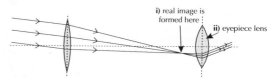

i) real image is formed here
ii) eyepiece lens

b)   The eyepiece lens is placed so that the real image formed
         by the objective lens is nearer to the eyepiece lens than its
         focal point. This means the eyepiece lens will produce an
         image that is magnified (and virtual and the right way up).
Q2 a) i) Large concave mirror: collects the parallel rays of light
         from an object in space and reflects it onto a smaller
         second mirror.
ii) Second smaller mirror: is placed in front of the larger
         mirror's focal point, and reflects the light from the larger
         mirror through a hole in the centre of the larger mirror.
         It focuses the light to form an image.
b)   The hole allows the light to go through from the small
         concave mirror. This means the observer can view the
         image, as the image is formed behind the large mirror.

18

P1a Topic 2 — The Electromagnetic Spectrum

P1a Topic 2 — The Electromagnetic Spectrum

Pages 113-114 — Electromagnetic Waves

Q1 a) True
b) False
c) True
Q2 Left to right: radio waves, microwaves, infrared, visible light, ultraviolet, X-rays, gamma rays.
Q3 Similarities — Any two from: e.g. both EM waves, both transverse, both travel at the same speed in a vacuum. Differences — e.g. different wavelength, different frequency.
Q4 a) 3×10^8 m/s
b) All electromagnetic waves travel at the same speed through a vacuum.
Q5 sunlight, prism, infrared, temperature, increased, hotter
Q6 a) i) white light
ii) prism
iii) silver chloride on paper strips
iv) stopwatch
b) Create a visible spectrum using white light and a prism. Silver chloride turns from white to black when exposed to light. Expose sliver chloride coated strips to each colour in the spectrum. Use a stopwatch to time how long each strip takes to turn black — record your results. The strips should change quickest nearer the violet end of the spectrum. Then place a strip in the area just past the violet part of the spectrum — this should see the quickest change of all. This shows there is an invisible form of light beyond this side of the visible spectrum.
c) ultraviolet radiation

Page 115 — The Dangers of Electromagnetic Radiation

Q1 a) microwaves
b) gamma rays
c) gamma rays
d) gamma rays
Q2 They can damage surface cells, which can lead to skin cancer and eye conditions.
Q3 a) High-energy ultraviolet radiation has nearly as high a frequency (and energy) as low-energy X-ray radiation, so is nearly as damaging.
b) Any two from: e.g. They can heat up the cells. / They can cause ionisation by colliding with molecules in the cells. / They can cause cell mutations which could lead to cancer. / They can kill cells.
Q4 a) Microwaves can heat body cells. People might be concerned that their brain cells may be heated up.
b) Infrared waves have a higher frequency than microwaves so could be more harmful. They can cause skin burns so it would be dangerous to hold it near your face.

Page 116 — Radio Waves and Microwaves

Q1 long-wave, short-wave, ionosphere
Q2 'Microwaves' are a spectrum of waves with different wavelengths. The wavelengths used in ovens are absorbed well by water molecules. Those used by mobile phones are not absorbed so well by water molecules — so the water in your cells doesn't get heated much.
Q3 a) This allows the satellite to send signals to (and receive signals from) a large area of the Earth.
b) Microwaves can pass through the Earth's watery atmosphere for use in satellite communications.
c) radio waves

Page 117 — Infrared Radiation

Q1 heat, hot, night-vision, dark, electrical, bright
Q2 a) i) True
ii) False (they are **reflected** along the fibre).
b) Infrared
Q3 a) i) E.g. grills and toasters.
ii) E.g. remote controls. Infrared is also used to link devices like computers and mobile phones over short-range distances.
b) Infrared sensors can detect an intruder's body heat and be used to trigger alarms or lights.

Pages 118-119 — Visible Light, UV and X-rays

Q1 a) We see objects because they are illuminated (they give out or reflect light). When light enters our eye, it gets refracted through the lens and focused onto the retina at the back of the eye. The retina then sends a message to the brain, which interprets the image.
b) A lens focuses visible light onto a light-sensitive film or electronic sensor that records the image.
Q2 a) It absorbs it and emits visible light.
b) Banks print fluorescent ink on banknotes. Under a UV light, genuine notes will display the special markings. Fake notes are usually printed on cheaper, slightly fluorescent paper, so they'll glow all over and have no special markings.
c) The ink in the pen would only be visible in UV light — this can help the police identify your property if it's stolen but would not affect the appearance of the object in normal light.
Q3 Water can be sterilised with UV radiation. The radiation kills viruses and bacteria that are in the water.
Q4 Although they do produce UV waves, these are mostly absorbed by special coatings inside the tubes so very little UV is emitted from the lights.
Q5 soft tissue, absorbed, bones, lead
Q6 a) True
b) True
c) False
Q7 1. Passengers' baggage can be X-rayed to check that no dangerous or illegal items are being taken on planes.
2. Passengers can be X-rayed to see if they are concealing any dangerous or illegal items on or in their body.

Page 120 — Gamma Rays and Ionising Radiation

Q1 kill, cells, cancer, focused, normal, ill, dose
Q2 a) True
b) Alpha, beta and gamma.
c) Ionising radiation is radiation that transfers enough energy to knock electrons off atoms.
Q3 a) gamma radiation
b) It kills insects and microbes which may make the fruit decay.

P1a Topic 3 — Waves and the Universe

Page 121 — The Solar System

Q1 Universe, Milky Way, stars, moons, Mercury, Jupiter
Q2 a) moon, planet, star, galaxy, Universe
b) 1 — Distance between Earth and Moon, 2 — Distance between Earth and Sun, 3 — Distance between stars, 4 — Distance between galaxies.

P1a Topic 3 — Waves and the Universe

Q3   The Universe doesn't contain all of the galaxies.

Page 122 — Is Anybody Out There?

Q1 a)   E.g. soil experiments
b)   E.g. The experiments are looking for any signs of life, such as bacteria.
c)   E.g. it's cheaper / it's more practical
Q2 a)   Using radio waves/microwaves.
b)   E.g. temperature.
Q3 a)   To look for life outside Earth.
b)   E.g. They survey radio waves from space and look for patterns which suggest intelligent life.
c)   By downloading the SETI screensaver which analyses radio waves.

Page 123 — Looking Into Space

Q1 a)   X-rays are absorbed by the atmosphere and can't be detected by ground based telescopes. By putting telescopes into space we can observe this type of EM radiation.
b)   E.g. Cosmic microwave background radiation.
Q2 a)   Improved magnification means we can look further into space and discover more and more galaxies.
b)   E.g. This has helped improve our understanding of the Universe as it allows us to collect more information about the universe. It also means that it is quicker and easier to increase our knowledge of the Universe.

Page 124 — Space and Spectrometry

Q1   slit, dark, wavelengths, elements, absorption
Q2 a)

light slit   eye slot
CD   slot for CD

b)   So that only light from the light source under test enters the light slit.
c)

The ordinary light bulb has a continuous spectrum with no black lines.

Page 125 — The Life Cycle of Stars

Q1 a)   heat (from thermonuclear fusion)
b)   gravity
c)   The force pulling the star inwards and the force pushing it outwards are equal, so they balance and cancel out.
d)   A main sequence star.
Q2 a)   Gravitational attraction pulls the material together.
b)   Energy is released when hydrogen nuclei fuse together to form helium nuclei/from thermonuclear fusion.
Q3 a)   It runs out of hydrogen.
b)   Its surface is cooler than a main sequence star's surface.
Q4   planetary nebula, white dwarf, supernova, neutron star, black hole

Pages 126-127 — The Origins of the Universe

Q1   energy/matter, matter/energy, explosion, expand
Q2 a)   The steady state theory says that the Universe has always been the way we see it today and always will be.
b)   It suggests that matter is being created as the Universe expands.
Q3 a)   It will sound lower pitched.
b)   The wavelengths of the sound will seem longer to Francesca as the ambulance moves away. This means the frequency will seem lower — creating a low pitched sound.
Q4   The light from distant galaxies has a lower wavelength than from those nearby.
Q5   The light we see from distant galaxies is at lower frequencies than that from near galaxies — it's shifted towards the red end of the spectrum. This tells us that all galaxies are moving away from us quickly — and so provides evidence that the whole Universe is expanding.
Q6 a)   CMB radiation is a low frequency electromagnetic radiation coming from all parts of the Universe.
b)   CMB radiation is cooling and dropping in frequency as the Universe expands and cools. This backs the Big Bang theory's idea that all the matter and energy was squashed into a very small space, before a huge hot explosion, followed by the expansion of the Universe.
c)   Red-shift provides evidence for the Big Bang theory as it shows that the Universe is expanding.
d)   The Steady State theory explains the red-shift of galaxies by saying that matter is being created in spaces as the Universe expands.
e)   Most scientists accept the Big Bang theory rather than the Steady State theory because it has more evidence supporting it, e.g. CMB radiation.

Pages 128-131 — Mixed Questions — P1a Topics 1, 2 & 3

Q1   The first two statements should be ticked.
Q2 a)   reflection
b)

TV remote sensor   mirror
normal
r
i
TV remote
angle of incidence, i = angle of reflection, r

Q3 a)   E.g. analysis of the soil for signs of life.
b) $v = f \times \lambda$, $\lambda = v \div f = (3 \times 10^8) \div (9.56 \times 10^7) = 3.14$ m
Q4 a)   Hydrogen nuclei combine (by thermonuclear fusion) to form helium nuclei. Over time more and more of the hydrogen is used up, producing more and more helium.
b)   E.g. The size of the star. / The amount of hydrogen contained in the star.
c)   No — this only happens to very massive stars and the Sun is not massive enough.
Q5 a)   1 — X-rays — E.g. Scanning for fractures/broken bones.
2 — Ultraviolet — E.g. Detection of forged bank notes.
3 — Infrared — E.g. To monitor temperature/night cameras/remote controls.
b) i)   Search for Extraterrestrial Intelligence.
ii)   Narrow band EM signals may have been sent from a transmitter and so from another life form, unlike most other wider band EM radiation from objects in space, e.g. stars.

P1b Topic 4 — Waves and the Earth

c) The further away a galaxy, the more its light is red-shifted. This shows that the more distant galaxies are moving away at a greater speed and so the Universe must be expanding.

Q6 a) Frequency = speed ÷ wavelength
= 3×10^8 m/s ÷ 1500 m = **200 000 Hz** (= 200 kHz).

b) Longer waves diffract more around large objects than shorter waves. So the long-wave radio signal diffracts around the mountains and can be received in Mr Potts' holiday cottage. The short-wave radio and TV signals (which also use short waves) don't diffract much and so they can't be received in his cottage.

c) They have different wavelengths/frequencies. The microwaves used for cooking are readily absorbed by water molecules (in the food) so that they heat the food. Those used in mobile phone networks are not absorbed much by water molecules, so they pass through clouds.

Q7 a) Gamma rays are directed carefully at the cancer at just the right dose so that they kill the cancer cells without killing too many normal cells.

b) Any one from: e.g. detecting cancer/sterilising food/sterilising medical equipment.

c) In general, the higher the frequency, the more dangerous the radiation.

d) Alpha and beta are two other types of ionising radiation. They are called 'ionising' because they bash into atoms and knock off electrons — which is known as ionisation.

Q8 a) The geocentric model says the Sun, Moon, planets and stars orbit the Earth. The heliocentric model says all the planets orbit the Sun, which is at the centre of the Universe.

b) Galileo's observations of Jupiter showed it had moons orbiting it. This showed not everything was in orbit around the Earth. This proved the geocentric model was wrong, and so gave evidence for the heliocentric model.

c) Improved magnification means we can find more galaxies and observe them more closely. Modern telescopes allow us to detect objects that aren't detectable using visible light — telescopes for other parts of the EM spectrum mean we can 'see' things that we couldn't before. Modern telescopes also work alongside computers to make it easier to collect and store huge amounts of data. They also make it quicker to analyse the data.

Q9 a) Refraction is when a wave bends or changes direction at the boundary between different materials.

b) E.g. A large concave mirror collects parallel rays of light from an object in space. It reflects them onto a second small convex mirror, placed in front of the large mirror's focal point. The smaller mirror reflects the light through a hole in the centre of the large mirror. A real image is formed behind the mirror. The real image is formed between an eyepiece lens and its focal point which means the eyepiece lens magnifies the image.

P1b Topic 4 — Waves and the Earth

Pages 132-133 — Ultrasound and Infrasound

Q1 body, media, reflected, detected, echoes, image, foetus
Q2 true, false, true, true
Q3 1 — The submarine emits waves of ultrasound.
2 — These ultrasound waves reflect off objects like other boats, the sea bed and marine animals.
3 — The reflected waves are detected as they arrive back at the submarine.
4 — Computers on board time the delay between emitting waves and detecting their reflections. They then use this to calculate how far away objects are.

Q4 a) The distance the pulse travelled is given by x = v × t
x = 1500 × 1 = 1500 m.
But that is for distance there and back — so halve.
So, x = 1500 ÷ 2 = **750 m**

b) The time will decrease — the wave has a shorter distance to travel.

Q5 a) Infrasound is sound with frequencies less than 20 Hz.

b) Infrasound waves have long wavelengths, so they can travel long distances and diffract around objects easily.

c) E.g.
Infrasound can be used to detect animal movements in remote locations using sensitive microphones./It can be used to detect meteor strikes and volcanic eruptions from far away.

Q6 The distance the pulse travelled is given by x = v × t
x = 1540 × 0.000045 = 0.0693 m.
But that is for distance there and back — so halve.
So, x = 0.0693 ÷ 2 = **0.03465 m** (= 3.465 cm).

Q7 The difference in distance travelled by the pulses is given by x = v × t
x = 1400 × (130 × 10⁻⁶)
x = 0.182 m.
This is twice the width of the crack, so the width of the crack is: 0.182 ÷ 2 = **0.091 m** (= 9.1 cm).

Page 134 — The Earth's Structure

Q1 The plates 'float' on the mantle. Convection currents in the mantle cause the plates to drift.

Q2 a) At plate boundaries, plates can slide past each other which sometimes causes an earthquake.

b) E.g. They look for a pattern of where and when earthquakes happen. / They use probabilities based on data from previous earthquakes.

c) This method isn't dead-on accurate — it isn't possible to predict the exact location or exact time of an earthquake.

Q3 a) The force of the masses pulling the brick will increase. This will eventually cause the brick to slip to the right.

b) It might take a different number of masses to make the brick slip. This is similar to a real earthquake because you can't really predict when it'll happen.

Pages 135-136 — Seismic Waves

Q1 seismic waves — shock waves from an earthquake
seismograph — a device that records seismic waves
P-waves — longitudinal seismic waves
S-waves — seismic waves that cannot travel through liquids

Q2 a) i) true
ii) true
iii) false
iv) false

b) iii) S-waves are **transverse** waves.
iv) Seismic waves can reflected **and refracted**.

Q3 a) As they travel through the Earth the density and other properties change gradually, causing a gradual change in speed. Change of speed causes change in direction, i.e. refraction.

b) There's a sudden change in the properties of the Earth. This causes some of the waves to be reflected, and some to be refracted — and they abruptly change direction.

c) They cannot travel through the Earth's core.

Q4 a) They travel at different speeds.

b) Trace A (P-waves travel faster and therefore arrive first).

c) It took between 2.5 - 3.5 minutes (150 - 210 s) for the wave to arrive. Taking the middle value of 3 minutes:
Distance = speed × time = 12 000 × 180 = **2 160 000 m** (2160 km). (Accept any distance in the range: 1800 km - 2520 km if it is supported by the correct calculation.)

P1b Topic 5 — Generation & Transmission of Electricity

d) Any two from: The amplitude would be smaller. / There would be no S-wave (it cannot travel through the core). / The P-wave would arrive later (it has further to travel).

Q5 a) E.g.

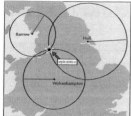

Draw three circles centred on the location of three seismometers — these are the distance arcs. Each circle's radius shows the distance between the seismometer and the earthquake's epicentre. The distance arcs from the three seismometers will cross at one place — the epicentre of the earthquake. This method is known as triangulation.

b) If only two seismometers are used, then their distance arcs will cross in two places, not one. So you won't be able to pinpoint the epicentre of the earthquake.

P1b Topic 5 — Generation & Transmission of Electricity

Pages 137-138 — Electric Current and Power

Q1 current, voltage, pressure, energy

Q2 Alternating current keeps reversing its direction back and forth. Direct current always flows in the same direction.

Q3 a) C
b) B
c) A

Q4 energy, watts, how long, power, current (or voltage), voltage (or current)

Q5 a) i) $P = I \times V = 0.43\,A \times 230\,V = \textbf{98.9 W}$ (a 100 W bulb)
ii) $P = I \times V = 0.17\,A \times 230\,V = \textbf{39.1 W}$ (a 40 W bulb)

b) Lamp A is likely to be brighter. (It has more power and therefore changes a greater amount of electrical energy into light in a given time.)

Q6

Appliance	Power (W)	Current (A)
Kettle	2600	**11.3**
Radio	13	**0.057**
Laptop computer	**736**	3.2
Lamp	**39.1**	0.17

Q7 a) ammeter, switch, battery, voltmeter, wires, test component
b) Set up the ammeter, switch, battery and component in a series circuit. Connect the voltmeter in parallel across the component. Close the switch and take a reading from the ammeter to get the current in the circuit, and from the voltmeter to get the voltage. Then use power = current × voltage to find the power of the component.

Pages 139-140 — Generating Electricity

Q1 voltage, moving, electromagnetic induction, magnet, coil, alternating, complete, magnetic, reverses

Q2 a) E.g.

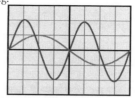

The trace should have a higher frequency and a higher amplitude.

b) E.g. Use a stronger magnet, use a coil with a larger number of turns, use a coil with a larger area.

Q3 As the wheels on the bike go round, they turn the magnet inside the dynamo. As Sebastian slows down, the magnet turns less quickly, which means less electric current is induced to power the lights.

Q4 a) larger
b) larger
c) smaller

Q5 a) E.g. By pulling the magnet out again (OR by turning the magnet round and pushing it into the coil OR by pushing the magnet into the coil from the left-hand side OR by turning the magnet around and pulling it out of the left-hand side of the coil).

b) E.g. By pushing the magnet in and immediately pulling it out again.

c) E.g. By rapidly pushing the magnet in and out of the coil a number of times.

Page 141 — Non-Renewable Energy and Power Stations

Q1 a) Non-renewable means that the resource will eventually run out/cannot be replaced when it is used up.

b) Nuclear power stations take a lot longer to set up than fossil fuel power stations.

Q2 a) E.g. Nuclear fuel is relatively cheap/it doesn't produce CO_2.
b) Nuclear reactors cost a lot to build and to decommission safely at the end of their useful life. It's also expensive to store or dispose of radioactive waste safely.

Q3 Acid rain... sulfur dioxide formed by burning oil and coal. Climate change... releasing CO_2 by burning fossil fuels. Dangerous radioactive waste... using nuclear power. Spoiling of natural landscapes... coal mining OR sulfur dioxide formed by burning oil and coal.

Q4 Answer will depend on student's opinion but should include an explanation of their reasoning, e.g. Lisa because nuclear power produces long-lasting, dangerous, radioactive waste.
Or Ben because nuclear power is carefully controlled to reduce any dangers and using fossil fuels adds to the carbon dioxide in the atmosphere, leading to climate change/an increased greenhouse effect/global warming.

Page 142 — Using Renewable Energy Resources (1)

Q1 Renewable means that the source of energy won't run out/can be replaced.

Q2 a) Tidal
b) Both
c) Hydro
d) Both

Q3 a) When the tide comes in the water passes through the turbines and then builds up behind the barrage. When the tide goes out the water is allowed out through the turbines in the barrage at a controlled speed. As the water passes through the turbines electricity is generated. (The water also turns the turbines on the way in.)

P1b Topic 5 — Generation & Transmission of Electricity

b) They can only be used in a few of the most suitable estuaries.

Q4 Any two from: e.g. High initial costs. / Spoiling the view. / Can be unreliable because it depends on winds. / It doesn't guarantee as much electricity as other methods. / May affect wildlife at or near the shore.

Page 143 — Using Renewable Energy Resources (2)

Q1 a) Any two from: e.g. they make a lot of noise. / They spoil the view/landscape. / They only work if it's windy.

b) Any two from: e.g. Once running, they don't create any pollution. / They use a renewable, free source of energy. / Running costs are low.

Q2 Disadvantages — they don't produce large amounts of energy, they don't work as well when it's cloudy. Advantages — they use a renewable and free source of energy (there are no fuel costs), they are a good way to provide energy in remote places.

Q3 a) **Geothermal** (The costs are higher for geothermal energy, because you need to drill into the Earth's crust.)

b) **Geothermal** (Burning biomass does release CO_2.)

c) **Biomass** (Geothermal energy is only possible where hot rocks lie fairly close to the Earth's surface.)

d) **Biomass** (The biomass in household rubbish can be burned to generate electricity.)

Q4 The amount of carbon dioxide released by burning the biomass is the same amount that was taken in by the plant as it grew. So overall the amount of CO_2 in the atmosphere doesn't increase.

Pages 144-145 — Comparison of Energy Resources

Q1 a) E.g. Gas will run out eventually. / Burning gas causes atmospheric pollution and contributes to the global warming.

b) E.g. High set-up costs. / High maintenance and/or decommissioning costs. / Long set-up times. / Dangerous radioactive waste. / Risk of catastrophic accidents. / Threat from terrorism.

c) E.g. large areas of fertile land are needed to grow biomass. / Atmospheric pollution when the gas is burned. Other answers are possible.

Q2 Answer will depend on student's opinion. 'I agree' could be backed up by mentioning that sea levels change in a predictable and reliable way, twice every day, and/or that the UK has a long coastline and plenty of opportunities to use the resource. 'I disagree' could be backed up by saying that there are only a few suitable estuaries.

Q3 Any two from: e.g. it's a reliable source of energy. / It doesn't release greenhouse gases. / We're not likely to run out of fuel any time soon.

Q4 a) The student could say that no pollution is produced when electricity is being generated. (Or that building the dams and manufacturing the turbines, generators etc. does cause pollution.)

b) The student could say that there are no fuel costs, or that building dams and purchasing turbines etc. is expensive.

c) The student might argue that dams are unsightly, they disturb the natural environment and disrupt wildlife etc. (Or they could argue that an impressive engineering structure has a positive visual impact.)

d) The student could say that it is rare for reservoirs to be empty even in dry weather, and water can be released to power the generators when it's needed most.

e) Any two from: e.g. it is a renewable source of energy. / It does not contribute to global warming (once running). / The output can be varied more quickly than that of most other power stations.

f) Any two from: e.g damage to wildlife habitats. / Set-up costs are high. / Set-up times are long. / Danger of the dam bursting.

Pages 146-147 — Electricity and the National Grid

Q1 1. Electrical energy is generated in power stations.
2. The voltage of the supply is raised.
3. An electrical current flows through power cables across the country.
4. The voltage of the supply is reduced.
5. Mrs Miggins boils the kettle for tea.

Q2 a) Transmitting electrical energy at high voltages improves the efficiency as heat loss is reduced. This saves more money than the cost of the equipment.

b) Step-up transformer.

c) A step-down transformer is used to reduce the voltage so that is at a safe, usable level for consumers.

Q3 E.g. High voltage in the power lines is a risk to people (e.g. flying a kite into a power line in the rain could be fatal)./ Some people are worried about the effects of longer- term health of people living near power lines (e.g. links with leukaemia have been suggested, but studies haven't yet found any conclusive evidence).

Q4 $V_P = V_S \times (N_P \div N_S) = 30 \times (25 \div 50) = 30 \times 0.5 = \textbf{15 V}$

Q5 a) The National Grid transmits energy at high voltage and **low current**.

b) A step-up transformer is used to **increase** the voltage of the supply (OR reduce the **current**) before electricity is transmitted.

c) Using a **low current** (OR high **voltage**) makes sure there is not much energy wasted.

Q6 a) A step-down transformer — they decrease voltages.

b) $N_S = N_P \times (V_S \div V_P) = 20\,000 \times (240 \div 400\,000)$
$= 20\,000 \times 0.0006 = \textbf{12 turns}$

c) $V_S = V_P \times (N_S \div N_P) = 400\,000 \times (10 \div 20\,000)$
$= 400\,000 \times 0.0005 = \textbf{200V}$

Pages 148-149 — Energy Efficiency & Cost-Efficiency

Q1 The power of an electrical appliance — kilowatt (kW)
The time an appliance is used for — hour (h)
The price of electrical energy — pence per kilowatt-hour
The electrical energy used by an appliance — kilowatt-hour (kWh)

Q2 a) kilowatt

b) power

Q3 a) $2 \times 3 = \textbf{6 kWh}$

b) $7 \times 6 = \textbf{42p}$

Q4 a) Payback time = £1200 ÷ £20 = **60 years**

b) No. Although the shutters are cheaper, they are less cost-efficient — they have a longer payback time.

Q5 a) i) Energy consumption = power × cycle time (in hours)
$= 2 \times 0.5 = \textbf{1 kWh}$

ii) Energy consumption = power × cycle time (in hours)
$= 2 \times 0.75 = \textbf{1.5 kWh}$

b) i) Energy used by Techno per year = 52 × 4 × 1 kWh
= 208 kWh.
Energy used by Sudso per year = 52 × 4 × 1.5 kWh
= 312 kWh.
Saving by using Techno not Sudso = 312 − 208
= **104 kWh.**

ii) 104 × 8p = **832p** (£8.32)

iii) Difference in price ÷ yearly saving = (£420 − £380) ÷ £8.32 = 40 ÷ 8.32 = 4.808 years ≈ **4.8 years**.

iv) Yes — the payback time is less than the expected life of the machine.

P1b Topic 6 — Energy and the Future

P1b Topic 6 — Energy and the Future

Page 150 — Energy Transfer

Q1 conservation, created, converted
Q2 a) **chemical energy** → heat energy.
b) electrical energy → **sound energy**.
c) **electrical energy** → **light energy**.
d) **elastic potential energy** → kinetic energy.
e) nuclear energy → **heat energy**.
Q3 a) i) chemical energy
ii) heat/thermal energy (and kinetic energy)
b) Any two from: e.g.
Chemical energy → heat energy (as the coal burns). /
Heat energy → kinetic energy (as the steam drives the engine). /
Chemical energy → light energy (in the lamp).
Q4 a) Gravitational potential energy.
b) Chemical energy from the porridge is converted to kinetic energy in Bruce's muscles and the moving bar. This kinetic energy is then transferred to gravitational potential energy.
c) It is converted into kinetic energy as it falls downwards.

Page 151 — Energy Transformations

Q1 a) True
b) True
c) False
d) True
Q2 a) 100 J
b) 5 J
c) 95 J
d) 5%
Q3

Total Energy Input (J)	Useful Energy Output (J)	Efficiency
2000	1500	**75**
4000	2000	50
4000	**1000**	25
600	200	**33**

Q4 The winch wasn't 100% efficient. Half of the input energy was wasted. Most of this is likely to have been heat or sound.

Pages 152-153 — Heat Radiation

Q1 a) False
b) True
c) True
d) False
e) False
Q2 a) Dark, matt surfaces are **good** absorbers and **good** emitters of heat radiation.
b) The best surfaces for radiating heat are **good** absorbers and **good** emitters.
c) The best materials for making survival blankets are **poor** absorbers and **poor** emitters.
d) The best surfaces for solar hot water panels are **good** absorbers and **good** emitters.
Q3 a) As it cools down, the tea is emitting more heat than it is absorbing.
b) It must be absorbing the same amount of heat that it is emitting.
c) A system that's at a constant temperature — radiates the same average power that it absorbs.
A system that's warming up — radiates less power than it absorbs.
A system that's cooling down — radiates more power than it absorbs.

Q4 a) i), ii) and iii)

Surface	Reading	Colour and Texture
A	10	matt black
B	4	dull silver
C	4	shiny white
D	2	shiny silver

b) Tim's experiment showed that of the four surfaces, the matt black surface was the best emitter of heat radiation. The shiny silver surface was the poorest emitter of heat radiation.
c) D because it absorbs (and will emit) the least heat and so will be best at keeping the food inside cool.

Pages 154-156 — Mixed Questions — P1b Topics 4, 5 & 6

Q1 a) E.g. Solar cells require little maintenance and no fuel, making them suitable for remote locations (where transporting fuel and arranging repairs would be difficult and expensive). / Solar power is a renewable source of energy and won't pollute the island.
b) light energy → electrical energy
c) E.g. wave power / wind power / hydroelectric power
Q2 a)

Type of lagging	Saving per year (£)	Initial cost (£)	Payback time (years)
Fibreglass wool	14.56	60	**4.12**
Material X	29.12	100	**3.43**

b) Material X is the most cost-efficient, as it has the shortest payback time.
c) E.g. Material X might be made from a silvered surface — these reflect nearly all heat radiation falling on them, which makes them good insulators.
Q3 a) P-waves — longitudinal waves
S-waves — transverse waves
b) refraction
Q4 a) Chemical energy.
b) Useful output energy = 1000 J – 100 J – 500 J – 50 J = 350 J. So efficiency = 350 ÷ 1000 = **0.35** (or 35%).
c) i) High voltage means low current (P = V × I). Keeping the current low means that less energy is wasted as heat in the cables.
ii) Step-down transformers are used to reduce the voltage of the supply before it reaches consumers in houses and factories.
Q5 a) Ultrasound — frequencies above 20 000 Hz.
Infrasound — frequencies below 20 Hz.
b) The distance the pulse travelled is given by x = v × t
x = 1520 × 3.2 = 4864 m
But that is for distance there and back — so halve.
So, x = **2432 m**
c) E.g. communications between animals.
Q6 a) P = I × V = 0.5 × 6 = **3 W**
b) Power = 40 W = 0.04 kW
Cost = power × time × cost of 1 kWh
= 0.04 × (4 × 7) × 13 = **14.6p**.
Q7 a) A current is induced because the coil experiences a varying magnetic field.
b) i) A
ii) A — alternating current, B — direct current
iii) Alternating current keeps reversing its direction back and forth. Direct current always flows in the same direction.
c) Advantages: e.g. will never run out. / Causes no pollution. / Has very low running costs. Disadvantages: e.g. spoils the view. / Environmental impact. / Depends on weather conditions.

ISBN 978 1 84146 722 1

SEHA44